DINOSAUR
JOKE BOOK

DINOSAUR JOKE BOOK

By SAM BERMAN

Library of Congress Catalog Card Number: 69-17282

1974 Printing

Copyright © 1969, by Grosset & Dunlap, Inc.

GROSSET & DUNLAP · NEW YORK

HOW DO YOU MAKE
A STATUE OF
A DINOSAUR ?

IT'S EASY. JUST GET A BLOCK OF MARBLE AND CHIP AWAY EVERYTHING THAT DOESN'T LOOK LIKE A DINOSAUR!

YOU REALLY SHOULD KNOW
MORE THAN THE DINOSAUR.

HOW DO YOU
KEEP A
TRACHODON
FROM
SMELLING ?

TRY CUTTING OFF HIS NOSE.

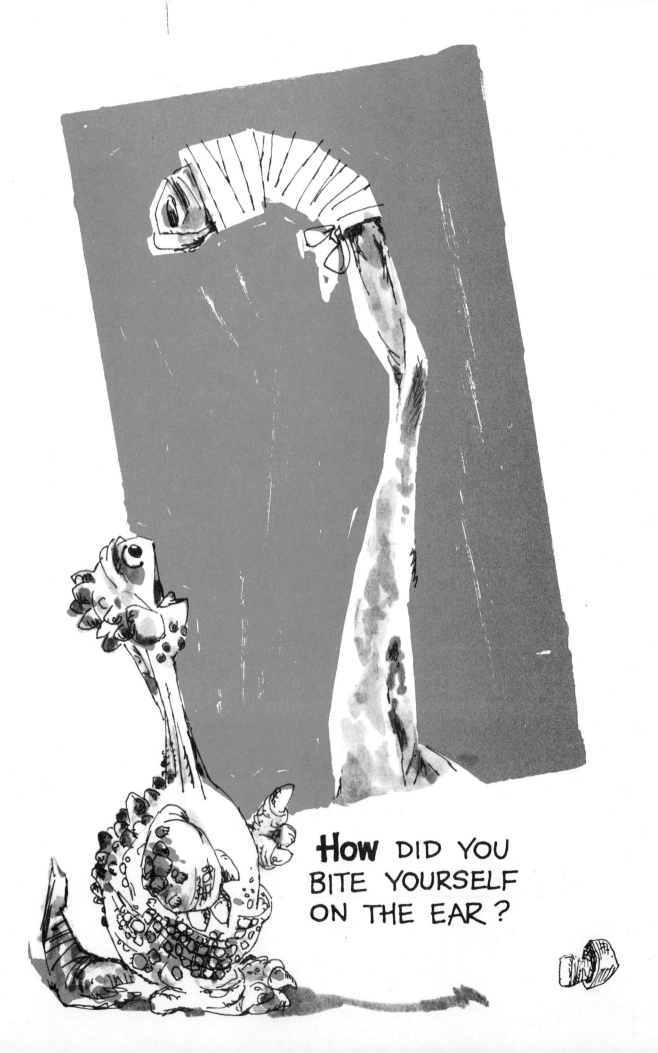

How DID YOU
BITE YOURSELF
ON THE EAR?

IT WAS EASY.
I STOOD ON A CHAIR.

WHY DOES
THE
PACHYCEPHALOPODUS
GO AROUND
HUMMING ALL
THE TIME?

WELL, HE DOESN'T
KNOW THE WORDS!

WHICH HAS MORE LEGS—

A DINOSAUR OR **NO** DINOSAUR?

NO DINOSAUR. NO DINOSAUR HAS EIGHT LEGS. A DINOSAUR HAS FOUR.

HOW WOULD
YOU RUN
OVER A
BRACHIOSAURUS
?

I'D START
AT HIS TAIL,

RUN UP HIS BACK,

THEN HIS NECK,

AND JUMP
OFF HIS
HEAD.

CAN YOU
IMAGINE
ANYTHING
NOISIER
THAN A
DINOSAUR
STUCK IN
A TREE?

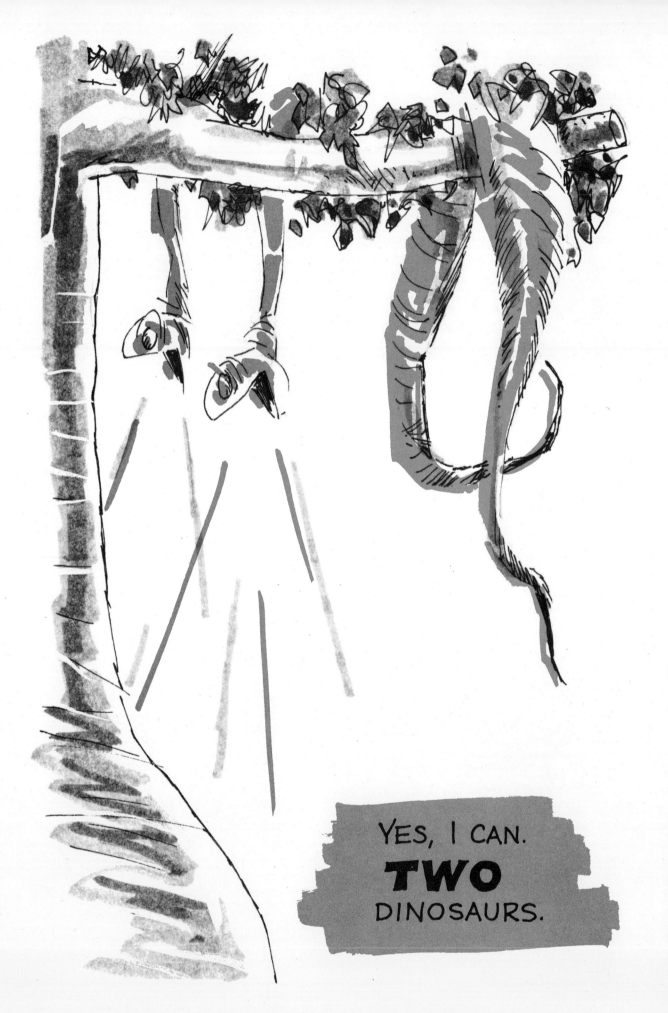

I'LL BET YOU CAN'T TELL ME WHAT A **TWIP** IS.

A **TWIP** IS A WIDE ON A TWAIN, SMARTY!

WHAT DID TARZAN
SAY TO BOY
WHEN HE
SAW AN OLD
STEGOSAUR
COMING TOWARD
THEM IN THE
FOREST?

OH, BOY, THERE'S AN
OLD STEGOSAUR
COMING TOWARD US
IN THE FOREST.

THAT PAIN IN YOUR
RIGHT LEG IS ONLY
OLD AGE.

NONSENSE, DOC—MY LEFT
LEG IS JUST AS OLD AS MY
RIGHT AND **IT** DOESN'T HURT!

WELL, HE SAT DOWN ON
AN ACORN. . .AND WAITED.

HOW DO YOU CATCH A BRONTOSAURUS ?

HIDE IN THE GRASS
AND MAKE A NOISE
LIKE A VEGETABLE.